0230/1000

Information without the invitations

THE UNKNOWN HIPSTER
DIARIES

by JEAN-PHILIPPE DELHOMME

AUGUST EDITIONS

First published in the United States of America in 2012 by

AUGUST EDITIONS
New York, NY
www.august-editions.com

This first edition is limited to 1,000 numbered copies
plus 50 A.P.s

© 2012 August Editions
© 2012 Jean-Philippe Delhomme

Design: Martine Trélaün / Design + Know-How

ISBN-13: 978-0-9859958-0-5
Library of Congress Control Number: 2012946796

2012 2013 2014 2015 / 10 9 8 7 6 5 4 3 2 1

Distributed to the U.S. by RAM Publications

Printed in China

Alternative transportation to the Punta della Dogana

The Venice Biennale

The Venice Biennale is to the art world what Milan is to the fashion crowd. The romantic types should stay away—the company of heavyweight collectors, egomaniac artists, and cynical critics is not for the fainthearted. Not to mention the harsh competition between secondary-market hipsters of all kinds.

I toughened myself for weeks with special-combat training and meditation. The program includes mental visualization exercises of forcing entry to exclusive events, survival skills like grabbing cocktail food in hostile environments, and of course sleeping at the occasional crash pad.

First, I dropped by the French pavilion to see what the great Claude Lévêque, artist of the famous and hilarious neon piece *Je suis une merde*, had planned for the national representation. But I decided to wait a few more days before visiting the more ascetic Bruce Nauman at the U.S. pavilion.

I was trying to concentrate on the Liam Gillick's installation at the German space when I got disturbed by a woman talking loudly on the phone about what she was going to wear that night to François's.

It irked me I had no invitation to the most sought-after event: the opening of the Punta della Dogana, the place François Pinault had founded to house parts of his immense collection and exhibit it to the public.

I didn't get discouraged by the fact that over a thousand influential people and art lovers had received invitations but me, and once in my best attire, I tried to hail a water taxi. Unfortunately, all the decent boats had been reserved for the invited guests.

Marc and Stella first thought I was some intruder sneaking in

Luckily I ran into a rogue performance artist, who, in the manner of the artist Swoon, had assembled various trash pieces into a floating barge. After negotiating a €150 "suggested donation" he agreed to take me on board. Normally crossing to the Giudecca takes only a few minutes, but we got caught in traffic on the Grand Canal, and my shoes and pants were soaked by splashing waves from the celebrities' speedboats rushing by.

We chose to dock behind the buffet, a place that seemed most discreet. Alarmed by the giant black flag waving above our vessel, or perhaps in fear of a seafood

With François Pinault

The elegant Patriarch of Venice

risotto shortage, a guest fiercely ejected me back to the sea. I recognized Marc, and begged for hospitality. And although I had been refused entry by a young and arrogant P.R. assistant at her last show in Paris, Stella personally helped me up the pier, and handed me a welcoming glass of prosecco.

"So, how's Tadao's work?" I asked, "Does it look good?"

But my new friends had disappeared, trapped in a crowd of admirers.

Spotting our host alone, I rushed to him, thinking it was good timing to greet him before the party takes off.

"Thank you for collecting so much art," I told him. "And this Punta is a really cool…"

"Would you mind stepping back?" a staff member interrupted me. "There are photographers at work behind you."

There was a line to enter the museum. But once in, only those alone were looking at the art. I spent a long time studying *Fucking Hell*, the monumental Jake and Dinos Chapman masterpiece. An older man, dressed like a priest, was one of the rare visitors, like me, to show more interest in the works displayed than in watching tycoons and supermodels.

"Are you wearing Alexander McQueen?" I asked.

"No, it's vintage Comme," he replied dryly.

It turned out he was a real cardinal. His position, he admitted, made him a frequent invite to this kind of event.

"I suppose the art world considers me a potential client," he said.

"Why do you think contemporary art is usually based on jokes?" I asked.

"Well, life's a joke, buddy. The serious bit comes after." Then he slapped my back. I was quite shaken, and went wandering in the next gallery.

There were rumors of a dinner hosted by Angela Missoni, in honor of (the less ascetic than I thought) Bruce Nauman, on a yacht. Following the crowd, I befriended a drunk oligarch who wanted to talk about his own collection.

"I got them all," he bragged. "The guy who does the handbags! The nurse painter! All of them!"

He was on the guest list, and we went on board together. The yacht was packed with the most beautiful girls, all shoeless so as not to harm the precious wood deck, which gave them a particularly unusual and dreamy coolness, but I intended to have at least one serious art conversation and headed to find the celebrated artist.

The charming Margherita Missoni

An avid art collector

Beautiful sunset in Biarritz

Natacha Ramsay in Arizona (after Olivier Zahm)

The Death of Dash Snow

I love surfing.

If you paddle a little farther out than the other surfers, beyond the break line, it will keep you away from the crowd and leave you plenty of time to read, think, or simply do nothing.

And at the end of the day, when everybody's gone, you just catch a wave back to the shore.

It was upon my return to civilization, when looking at the *Purple Diary*, that I realized all that happened when I was surfing.

While Terry was busy shooting a Pirelli calendar, Olivier was kissing more girls in a night than most people in their entire life. And he was also taking hundreds of new photographs of the sexy Natacha Ramsay in unexpected locations.

And this is how I learned about the death of Dash Snow, the fantastic artist with the fantastic name. Before I read Glenn's beautiful eulogy, I only knew of Dash through pictures in a 2008 issue of *Purple*.

Dash Snow (after Purple)

Dash Snow in his Bowery studio (after Purple)

Even the hipsters I questioned at the time were uncertain when it came to describing Dash's work. Some said he was doing Polaroids. Others said that he was handsome. "You have no idea with the beard, but he is incredibly handsome!"

But even if you haven't seen his collages or anything else, you could tell he was a true artist by these photographs, just like when you see a picture of Marcel Duchamp playing chess, Jackson Pollock in his paint-dripped shoes, or Picasso proudly standing in his briefs.

The effect is the same with images of Dash choosing an LP, drinking a beer in bed, or wearing a dress.

For this is how you know you are confronting a real artist: when you feel a little square or slightly overcautious.

(By the way, on my last day of surfing, I flooded my iPod while listening to "Perfection as a Hipster," by God Help the Girl.)

Repair Kits

Last week, when the art crowd jostled into a thousand openings in Chelsea, I sailed off to Governors Island for the inauguration of *Pioneers of Change*, a festival of Dutch design, architecture, and fashion.

After a short crossing from the southern tip of Manhattan we landed on this strange island, with its abandoned military and administrative buidings and ghost housing for the officers. The sky was gray, about to rain, and there was something a little sinister in the air, which suddenly made me fear being taken into custody and held in an endless quarantine.

Eleven identical former officers' houses were the scene of installations and work-shops by Platform 21, the Dutch art and design collaborative. It was funny to think of the regimented life that had probably ruled these rooms where Christien Meindertsma's giant knitted works now lay on the wooden floor.

Repairing was the main theme of the festival. In one of the houses' kitchen, a calm, blonde woman was mending plates she had purposely broken and gluing together the slightly misplaced parts in an artful arrangement. In another room, a young artist was selling repair kits for damaged walls with yellow, red, and blue tapes to be applied in Mondrian patterns.

On board the Governors Island ferry

Amazing knitting installation

But the best repairing kit was a wool filler for mending holes in clothing, by the designer Heleen Klopper.

I immediately used it to fix the elbows of my old, worn-out jacket from a Sydney thrift shop.

And then I repaired a sweater I had brought with me.

More wool

Upgrade to classic British style with elbow patches

Ingenious repair, not food stains!

My old jacquard, revamped.

Night was falling, and I returned on the ferry. Disappearing high into the clouds and darkness and as if drawn by memory into the hollow sky, were the silhouettes of the Twin Towers in projecting lights.

Bowling with
Tom Sachs

A bit ago I was taken to a little party at Tom Sachs's studio by my friend Glenn.

We were greeted by Tom wearing desert fatigues and his signature gray T-shirt. If you didn't know it was him, a piece of tape with his name handwritten on it was stuck on his chest: Tom. He then wrote our names on tape and stuck them on our jackets. Everybody had their name written on tape, as if it's a convention of sorts.

If you'd never been to Tom's studio, it's 30 percent hardware store, 60 percent art gallery, and the remaining 10 percent a miscellaneous mix of accounting, archives, and research. The hardware space also includes a small kitchen with a lot of funny signs on the fridge, cornflakes, bananas on a plate—which could make it an installation piece ready for sale at Gagosian, except that it's a real kitchen, meaning a working one. At least, it looks like one. Everything else in this room was endless fun to look at: Tom's tools, Tom's chain saws, Tom's cameras, and Tom's classic Hello Kitty sculptures on the shelf.

I had gone there many years before, also taken by Glenn, when only the hardware space existed. It was a launch party for Tom's Chanel guillotine. People were drinking and talking, not paying that much attention to the life-size guillotine with the famous fashion house logo. Then Tom brought out a pork roast he had cooked and placed it where you were supposed to put your head if you were given a death sentence. Tom pulled on a rope to release the knife and it came down with a brief and sinister whistle that not only cut the roast, but the metal tray on which it was presented. I remember juice splashing on people around it, particularly on a romantic, pale, and dark-haired young woman, dressed in 1930s vintage and who looked like she could be a poet, or at least someone with a tormented interest in the art world.

Shortly after this semiprivate event, Tom's work became more and more famous, while Chanel's celebrity remained more or less the same.

At today's party, we found out that the studio has a basement, where unused parts and remains of installations are stacked along the walls. Tom had also installed a makeshift bowling lane, and a few guest were participating.

It made the same thundering noise when the ball rolled and hit the pins, just like real bowling alley.

When I gave it a try, I realized it could be a metaphor for artistic success: bowling over the art world! And although I have never bowled before, I knocked over all the pins on my first attempt.

"Is bowling big in France?" Andy asked me.

Andy bowling

Unknown technique

Bill Cunningham and the Pumpkins

So I went to the Union Square farmers market this morning. I really don't like going there so much, but I thought it's the only place I could find rhubarb this time of the year.

The place is a bit ridiculous. People have the same exaggeratedly receptive, wide-eyed expression as when they are walking into a Chelsea art gallery, as if buying smoked bacon from the Flying Pig Farm has the same authority of an art critic selecting a new artist's monograph. And let's not mention those couples who block the path with their baby strollers and dogs. They spend hours trying to single out the perfect carrot, or the most organic apple pheasant sausage for their non-vegan dog.

It's worse during Fashion Week, when young models with rubber boots, infinite legs, and big knitted sweaters hold bunches of fresh-cut flowers tightly against their chests, as if they were in the working garden of a Scottish estate or a Moscow suburb dacha—straight out of a Tim Walker story for *Casa Vogue*.

Although this week was not Fashion-Anything, I immediately spotted the famed cobalt blue of Bill Cunningham's workwear jacket. He was strolling among the crowded stands looking at the humanity and vegetables with the same gentle and amused smile.

It was so comforting to see such an original and authentic character as the legendary Bill, with his discreet 35mm Nikon, in such an artificial surrounding!

I asked him if I could take a little snapshot, he graciously obliged, and then he slipped away after a little pat on my shoulder.

Minutes later, as I was plotting my escape route through the back of a farmer's stand, I saw Bill suddenly aiming his camera at a stack of pumpkins in front of me. For a second, I saw on his face that unemotional stare of a predator, while shooting at light speed. I am sure that most fashion celebrities and famous socialites photographed by Bill are probably too self-focused to notice this cat-catching-a-mouse stare. They should feel like an ordinary orange pumpkin.

The Marni Mystery
Fashion Bum

I was walking down Mercer this morning when I thought I saw a fellow hipster standing in the shadow. He was holding a number of Marni shopping bags, some of them hanging from a walking stick carried on his shoulder. His hood and oversized bead necklace gave him the look of a mystic, a bit of a cool pilgrim.

I then realized he was pausing for two fashion beings: a photographer and a stylist who were giggling in excitement. Were they accessorizing the hobo or was it a hipster dressed as a surreal bum? Or were they stealing ideas from a true (hip) bum?

On the stairway was a scattered stack of various junk and discarded shopping bags from the nearby Marni store—the bum's temporary belongings, but could very well have been the female stylist's ammunition. She kept picking up new bags to try them on the model.

Finally she brought a little white dog, which might have been the bum's own.

Maybe the dude was an old friend? Maybe he was a well-paid bum or a supermodel working for free? My guess is that they were trying to make a political fashion statement, something they wouldn't have done for a serious magazine.

Perhaps it was purely visual.

Dogs also like to dress as hipsters

Halloween Dog Parade

Graphic black-and-white

On my way to the flea market in Dumbo on Sunday, I came across a little Halloween dog parade on the Promenade of Brooklyn Heights.

Costumed dog parades are to fashion what outsider art is to the Gagosian Gallery.

Banal entries

A studious jury

But outsiders are no less committed than professionals. They believe so much in their creations that they proudly strutted in them, instead of hiding backstage to only appear at the very end.

There were several amateur photographers documenting the event, one crouching dangerously close to a pit bull's jaws. (You might want to check for photos and a full report on Style dog dot com).

A poodle doesn't need a lot to look gorgeous

Pumpkin allover

The Alice Cooper wig gives
this pitbull a sweet look

Rottweiler in a satin cape

These nervous greyhounds remind me of young, timid fashion editors

I then skateboarded down to the flea market. There was a beautiful autumn light, which made the vintage cars in the parking lot look even more like Stephen Shore photographs. If you can't afford a print, maybe you can drive an original.

I was in search of a vintage peacoat for the winter when I spotted a theater mask of a horse. It has a patient, melancholic expression, with a hint of craziness in the eyes, just like a real horse.

Maria and Mark at the flea market

I was imagining the avant-garde productions in which the horse mask would have been used seventy years ago when I bumped into Maria Cornejo and Mark Borthwick. They have that free-spirit, illuminated faces of real artists, and outshined everybody else around them with a mien of natural fantasy. Mark was carrying a small, carved wooden canoe he has just bought. It seems like just the right accessory for his pictures or music.

Will with his bakery apron and "Candy Clouds" painting

Will's Bakery

Will Cotton is a painter, but when he is not producing his voluptuous and airy paintings he bakes delicious sweets and cakes, which transforms the viewer in an eater—satisfying his desire to bite into a candy cloud (or the irresistible tender parts of a pale model) by bringing home a real meringue or a pink macaron.

For this purpose, he has set a pop-up bakery in the back of Partners and Spade.

I know many tedious installation artists who, if they'd indulge themselves in doing something else, would rather built a mock-up hardware store in a museum space and sell nails and bolts. The more theorical ones would install a video recording studio, where viewers would be encouraged to tell shameful stories.

The more socially and politically concerned artists would force visitors to sip a full bowl of a soup made with heterogeneous ingredients ten thousand viewers from various communities would have been invited to bring.

Rose and all the aides were wearing tiaras

An emaciated, successful young artist from east London, with feverish eyes, dark long hair, and an animal skin-dress would lead a taxidermy workshop, with birds and mice found in an abandoned barn covered with graffiti.

And think of the art some full-time patissiers would do. Gloomy neo-expressionism? Post-Koons? Naive-Peyton? One thing is sure, the most hazardous attempts would be if they tried to imitate Will.

Andy and Jean-Michel

Philosophy on the Go-Go

It is quite fantastic to think that once upon a time at Indochine people like Andy Warhol or Jean-Michel Basquiat were sitting in these very same booths, beneath the banana leaf murals and eating the very same delicious entries. (Although I don't know if they were really into eating.)

It used to be a place for artists, my friend Glenn told me.

Nowadays it's more the fashion crowd who haunt the scene. Once I asked Glenn what he thought of the opening of a young artist, which got the same amount of coverage as a new Prada store: "Yeah, but art & fashion are more or less the same thing," he said.

Friday night was Indochine's twenty-fifth anniversary party.

I skipped a philosophy lecture to arrive early. Some people were already waiting anxiously outside the temporary tent, and then once inside we queued in front of the stairs into the restaurant. At irregular intervals the charming Nadine Johnson would appear from behind the curtains, and with the magnaninous power of a blonde goddess saved a few human beings by letting them in.

With a moustache Hamish revealed an entirely different personality

The tenebrous Lady Fag

Casey, one of the best-dressed
men of the night, was wearing
a 10-dollar thrift-store suit

The amazing Sophie-Anne, from Paris

The elegant and cool Jean-Marc,
hero of the party

Todd was wearing his signature
semi-deconstructed straw hat

Once saved, I elbowed my way to the center of the crowded room shaking with loud music. But most of the guests were too gorgeous—or too tall, as is the case with some of the superstar drag queens—to be pushed on the side, and I finally had to retreat in the basement bar and dance floor, which some insiders refer to as Under-chine and had not seen open for decades.

I'm not of the type who dances until he falls flat on his back and needs to be carried to the emergency room. I would rather talk to someone, so I went up to the go-go dancer poles and asked one of the prettiest go-go girls if it would bother her if we had a little chat while she was working. This was not an absurd question, since we all know that in New York and Paris there's a sign in buses saying that you're not allowed to talk to the driver. Not at all, she said, although we had to shout over old B52s tunes alternating with electronic beats. It turned out that, as most folks working below 14th Street, she was a professional artist, and go-go danced to pay for her studio space. But apparently she also does volunteer go-go. Nude dancing is often frowned upon by serious people, especially from the very earnest crowd, but go-go volunteering is the most rewarding part of her career, she added, unlike talking.

Carine, André, and Anna

Gabi and Adi

Thom

Andy

Anthony

Gina

Glenn

Mathias

My Life as a Model

I have recently been offered to do some modeling for French *GQ*.

I was worried I would need to lift weights or swim two hours a day to get in shape, but they said it was okay to stay as I am.

Modeling involves very little actual work, and there's nothing demeaning about it if you work with tasteful photographers. A lot of the job is waiting around, and while most people in the studio spend their day checking Facebook, it's not forbidden to read a book or write poetry while you're worked on by the hairdresser or have your nails polished.

It's a known fact that fashion photographers have big egos, but it's okay not to talk to them. There is always loud music in the studios, and photographers can hardly hear themselves giving directions anyway. And this is okay too, because their comments are generally very basic, like "gorgeous," or "yes!" Actually, if you happen to hear them over the noise, their comments are more embarrassing than anything else. They suddenly make you think the whole enterprise is not serious, but it is.

Here are some of my favorite shots, with behind-the-scenes commentary and my own tips.

This was for the November fashion story. While posing with these logs, I had a great talk with the girls. Natasha, the blonde on the left, had studied philosophy in Moscow, while Prune, on the right, had just published a novel. It turned out both girls had been featured naked in *Purple Diary*, which disappointed me a bit.

For an air travel editorial. I'm so relaxed when I model, I can actually fall asleep for real. I walked out of the shoot with these expensive pajamas, and had to return them to the assistant the next day, but they shrunk down three sizes since it was raining and I couldn't find a cab.

Who said modeling was a tough job? I remembered I just had some delicious bruschetta from catering, and the only thing that bothered me on the shoot was the scratchy feel of this rare vinyl on my fingers.

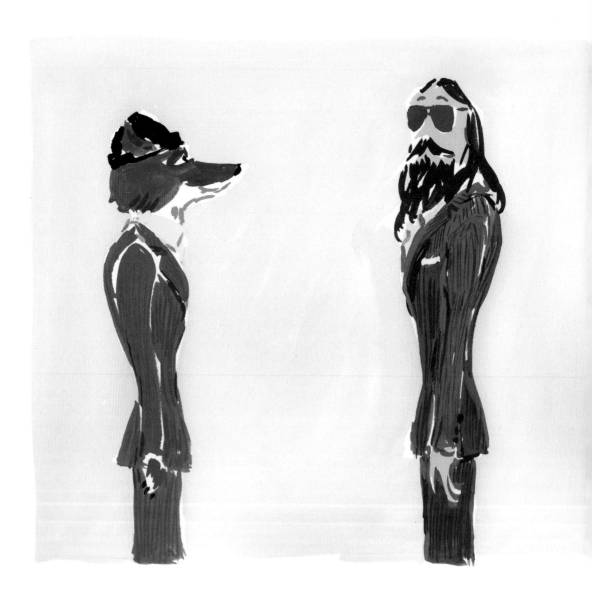

A tribute to *Fantastic Mister Fox*, one of my favorite movies, ever.

Another cool shot. I almost forgot the photographer was there.
If the stylist wants to play, I'm able to completely transform myself.

A few tips for modeling:
1) No sports.
2) Sleep as much as you want, or don't.
3) Extract respect from the assistants by insisting on your musical tastes.

Like Karl, Damien wears lots of Gothic rings with skulls and gargoyles

Damien Hirst and the *End of an Era*

Damien Hirst is one of those rare artists who can, once in a while, produce an artwork that gains more instant awe than the new Ferrari parked on the street.

And he is one of the few artists today who challenge money and power with ways that speak at equal level to the most wealthy and powerful.

A master of Vanitas, he always find entertaining ways to remind the viewer that death and diamonds—no matter how many or big—are nothing.

Judgement Day, a thirty-foot-long gold cabinet filled with 30,000 manufactured diamonds, is an ironic slap in the face of the shallow, and a consolation for the broke.

Ancient Greek philosophers—and more recently, psychedelic gurus—used the same rhetoric to one-up kings and rich merchants, but somehow with less efficiency than an entire shark, or a bull's head, submerged in formaldehyde solution.

The exhibition is called *End of an Era.* I don't know if it refers to some political or financial pronouncement about the end of our era, or if it states that a particular body of Damien's own work had come to an end.

This bow tie works well with dots.

Rose's necklace echoes the diamond paintings

Although the opening was on a Saturday, the uptown gallery (limos waiting outside) was buzzing with famous artists and important people.

The only sure way to know if somebody was less well-known was to see if he was taking pictures of others. Come to think of it, a lot of people were actually taking pictures of each other, like at an entrance of a fashion show.

Damien was surrounded by people asking for autographs and handing to him various books or objects to be signed. A skateboarder even had a new Damien Dots skateboard signed. I couldn't see if he drew a big skull on it, as he did for some of the other fans.

A simple Post-it signed by Damien

Mick walking along "Judgement Day"

It turned out that the only discreet viewer was the real rock star. Mick Jagger was in a dark crewneck sweater worn under a navy suit. Why does he looks so cool? Of course, he has seen it all. Even Jean-Luc Godard himself filmed the Rolling Stones recording "Sympathy for the Devil." But while *One Plus One* could have been the coolest documentary, JLD got carried away by vanity, French intellectualism, or some girlfriend's advice, and added all the revolutionary theories sequences that required so much coffee for the viewer.

Unlike Damien's works.

Karl's Little Advice

Karl and I are the most opposite human beings one could imagine, but I often find my point of view closer to his than I'd have thought, and it's not only megalomania. Besides that, I have an history with Karl.

Back in the '90s I was once assigned by the underground magazine *Murmur* (it has disappeared since, outpowered by glossies like *Purple*) to report from Karl's studio at the house of Chanel. I observed the last fitting before the runway show, where Karl was reviewing and giving the last touches to his dresses, and surrounded by collaborators, muses, and advisers such as Victoire de Castellane, Amanda Harlech (who had left her horses for the day), and some of the world most prestigious editors-in-chief. Everybody was so serious, the only fellow with whom I could share a momentary friendship was Michel Gaubert, the famous DJ, who modestly showed me the cassette tape on which he had laid down music for the show the night before: "A little of Mozart, a little of something else," he said. I should have been thrilled to be where no one is allowed, and in a sense I was (although I would have prefered to witness Allen Ginsberg reading "Howl" for the first time, or being second camera assistant for Jean-Luc Godard, or especially being an intern at the Factory in its glorious days), but somehow, I couldn't concentrate on the action, distracted by Camille Miceli, the head of Chanel PR at the time. In high boots, mini skirt, and tight T-shirt, she was asking me if I needed anything. I was

hynotized. (She would one day pose nude for *Paradis*, Thomas Lenthal's magazine.) At the fitting Philip Treacy, the great hat designer, was gracefully slouching in his casual outfit, while I had stupidly traded my worn-out jeans and thrift-store plaid shirt for a navy power suit paired with a red tie, in an attempt to fit in to the couture mode. The red tie was the mistake, and when I was finally introduced to Karl, it was to hear: "Oh, I thought you were the security man, looking after the jewelry!" Anyone would have been embarrassed to death (and well, I can't say I wasn't), but I survived, and understood that I had been gifted with the most exclusive style advice ever.

Now, whenever I come across an interview with Karl, I read it meticulously! There's always a lot to learn. The most recent one was in the May issue of *Interview* magazine, where the model Sigrid Agren asked his advice on how to become a supermodel.

Lagerfeld: "[..] You want to know what the real secret is?"

Agren: "Tell me."

Lagerfeld: "It's not being perfect."

A Dreary Saturday in Chelsea

A tormented, Burchfield-esque vision presented itself on a Chelsea street on Saturday, when the sinister weather put gallery visitors to the test. The actual and somewhat less torturous Charles Burchfield graphite drawings were on view at the nearby D'Amelio Terras Gallery.

Rubber hunting boots, worn in various colors, brought a cheerful note to the dark mood of the day, while the melting snow left a handful of art lovers stranded on the slouchy snow banks with little chance of rescue from gallery assistants.

Ironic wiring in a Banks Violette installation at Gladstone—a sculpture that somehow formally echoed my hat. Being in a mundane state of mind, I wondered how one could vacuum between the wires without messing up the piece.

Band of Bikers at ZieherSmith presents a hundred fading 1970s snapshots of gay bikers found by the gallery owner in his building basement, among the discarded belongings of a recently deceased tenant.

I wonder where Hell's Angel cap went.

Fashion Week Preview

This is the time of the year when you see them returning to New York: the tall, thin, black silhouettes navigating the slush in their cheap Rock boots. They announce the coming of Fashion Week like quails announce the end of summer.

I was inspired to write them a poem :

I see you, all pale-faced and sad eyes, standing at the corner.

Don't look at me unless you're Vinoodh and Inez.

My boyfriend, he will get you.

Dump you in a trash bin somewhere.

Daddy will drop you in a pond behind the factory.

I saw you walking fast

Holding tight the frozen plastic of the look books

And now in the middle of the night

I hear you giggling in the hotel rooms.

I often see this guy at the airport. He chaperones the girls transatlantic. I think he figures out the passports, waits for the bags, makes sure some jerk doesn't snap some photos of them in their sleep.

The girls look bored while they wait. No friends, only a cellphone.

Zero + Maria Cornejo

New York
Fashion Week

It was a bright winter morning as I walked on 11th Avenue toward 36th Street, along the construction-site fences and the snow-covered sidewalks. I even spotted a tiny bird enthusiastically twittering on top of an orange construction sign. I imagined he was announcing spring, or at least in anticipation of its arrival.

I rarely spend time in this part of the city, and the small industrial buildings, the repair garages, the wide-open spaces, and the newly built high-rise condos against the Hell's Kitchen backdrop in the distance all reminded me of some verses from Apollinaire's poem *Zone*.

J'ai vu ce matin une jolie rue dont j'ai oublié le nom

Neuve et propre du soleil elle était le clairon

. . .

Les inscriptions des enseignes et des murailles

Les plaques les avis à la façon des perroquets criaillent

J'aime la grâce de cette rue industrielle

Hosfelt Gallery—where the Zero + Maria Cornejo presentation was taking place, on the second floor of an automotive parts and car-repair shop—is a beautiful, luminous space, with a pure, natural light that seemed the perfect translation of Maria's spirit.

.

The next day I headed over to the Moncler Gamme Bleu presentation. One hundred or so models were standing on a four-story scaffolding structure installed in the golf driving range on the Hudson, wearing the latest Moncler collection.

The futuristic, neo-military opera-style installation reminded me of the aesthetic of Thierry Mugler's ad campaigns from the late '80s.

The coldness was extreme, and only the well-equipped could stay on the tall balconies to study the models and confront the chilly winds blowing from across the river in the New Jersey dark skies.

I was glad to be wearing my vintage Moncler and the French ski-team hat that I had bought the previous weekend from the Brooklyn flea market to attend the fashion shows. This is where I saw Ricky, who was freezing, simply wearing a corduroy jacket and his marine captain's cap.

"This is almost model cruelty," he said, alluding to the arctic endurance test unfolding on the scaffolding.

Ricky forgets, however, the extreme high-tech yet stylish insulation of the Moncler design (you can ski in comfort and still feel like a page from *Wallpaper* magazine).

"Don't worry," I told him, "these pretty young things feel as hot as they would in a *Purple* fashion shoot."

John Pawson's
Monastery

On my way to the Milan Salone this year, I made a meditative stop at Novy Dvur, the iconic minimalist monastery designed by John Pawson in the Czech Republic.

Here is a recorded excerpt of the conversation I had with one of the anonymous monks.

Unknown Hipster: "In 1999, when the news was announced that the minimalist architect John Pawson had designed a Cistercian monastery, I was fascinated ..."

Monk: "Do you mean fascinated by the monastic life, or by the minimalist architecture?"

"Both! It is such the perfect match! The architect serves an elevated purpose, and the pure lifestyle of his clients validates the architecture in return."

"You don't think it works the same when an architect designed a lavish house for a celebrity?"

"I'm amazed that as monks you had the idea to choose Pawson."

My own monklike uniform for the Milan Salone del Mobile

"One of us had wandered into the Calvin Klein store in New York, which had been designed by John. It was so pure. Nothing distracted from the product. It was shopping taken to a religious level. Wouldn't it make a wonderful monastery, we thought, if we replace fashion with God?"

"You must have been a dream client ..."

"In fact, unlike Calvin, we had a restricted budget, but this didn't stop us from having many discussions with John."

"Minimalism is a luxury. It's much sought after by those who have everything."

"Just like us; we have nothing, but we have everything."

"Did you think of having a fashion designer designing the robes?"

"It was discussed. Although I'm not sure it would give the same credibility to the designer as it gave to the architect."

"What about tableware? Did you have someone designing the plates and bowls?"

"Are you now confusing the monastery with a boutique hotel?"

"Speaking of which, you must be constantly disturbed by architecture fanatics and style hunters ...?"

"We do have people coming in search of a spirituality, which is not always easy to find in all those flagship stores by prominent architects. Some are just looking for ideas to build their own minimalist house. I don't blame them, although they probably should just look inside themselves."

"Would you recommend to those saturated by materialism to do a retreat at Novy Dvur?"

"Maybe not. They may become infected with the architecture obsession."

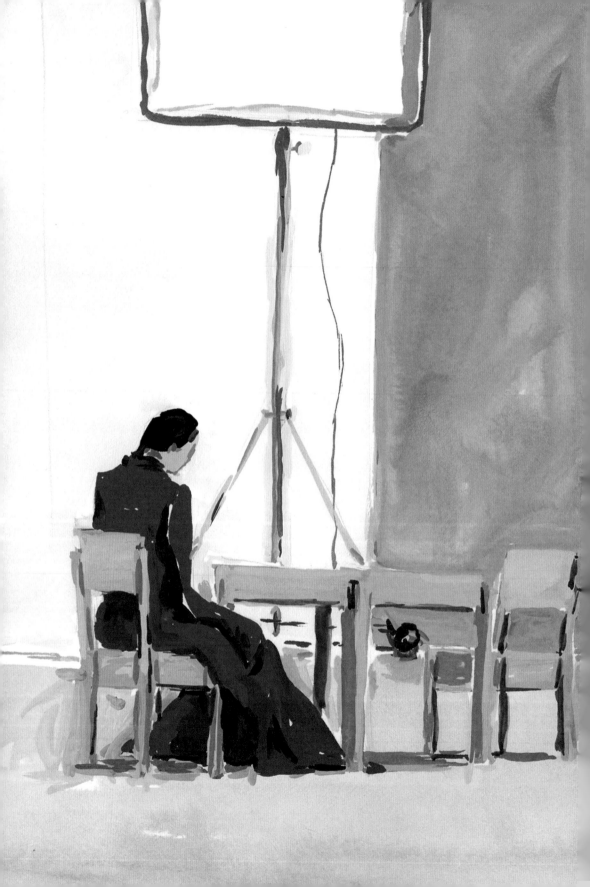

The Artist Is Present

It was not without anxiety that I went to *The Artist Is Present*, Marina Abramovic's exhibit at MoMA.

I had always feared that performance art would require a lot of patience, or specialized knowledge, like the kind needed to understand some Japanese dances. And I have this big book on feminist art—which I bought on a day I felt devoted to the 1970s—with photographs of performances I'm glad to never have endured.

What to expect from a woman who, since the '70s, has constantly exposed herself to danger, disgust, or boredom, and played with Sex and Death. This morning, a friend remarked that art is always about Death, but it's one thing to do a gloomy painting on a rainy day, and another to cut yourself with knives, hold snakes, and scrub skeletons.

On a happy spring Saturday afternoon, I finally joined the peaceful crowd of tourists and art lovers at MoMA.

On entering the museum's atrium, I saw Marina in her red gown.

It was stunning.

She was sitting alone, her face in her hands, with the facing chair unoccupied. Standing on the perimeter of the rectangular area, visitors were silently looking, in awe, as if witnessing the last moments of a saint or a beloved outer-space queen. I personally felt sorry for Marina that nobody would dare sit in the empty chair. Summoning my courage, I considered walking up to the table so that, at the very least, the artist wouldn't be present for nothing.

But before I could commit, a short, plump woman slipped in, moving silently as if she had been walking in her socks, and was already in the chair.

She sat down stiffly, her feet firmly on the ground, hands flat on her knees, with an expression of calm submission and awareness, as if attending an examination or a yoga class for the first time.

Marina still had her face in her hands. Was she asleep? Or in profound pain? Or intolerably bored with the museum institution, or the idea of Art itself? I sensed she might suddenly stand up, kick her chair, slap the participant's face, and leave, never to return.

Instead, she slowly lifted up her head, and started to gaze at her observer.

Walking to the other side of the perimeter, I realized that what I had originally taken for a dense group of viewers was, in fact, a line. It's not because performance art is imbued with the spirit of 1970s happenings that there was no order here. Or maybe it was adapted to today's standards of order. More likely, it was part of the ceremony and constraints within which the visitor was invited to take part.

I confirmed this insight with a tall brunette next to me, who was writing in a notebook wearing a very Salinger pale green dress. Helen was an art student from Maryland, and she had indeed been in line for two and a half hours.

"Are you afraid?" I asked.

"Afraid ?... No. Well, I guess, yes, a little bit."

"I think it takes courage!"

Because who knows what's going to happen once one is left alone with his inner self under imaginary scrutiny?

In the distance, opposite to the person facing Marina, was the photographer Marco Anelli. He sat behind a telephoto lens, similar to those used to capture wildlife or celebrities sunbathing on a private island.

He has been documenting the performance since it began, and clocks the same hours as Marina. All his close-ups of the participants are on the exhibit's website, and it's the most astonishing body of work.

A strange collection of faces, some illuminated, some in tears, some lost in the void, and a few trying to aggressively dominate. There's even a priest (one wonders if he is mentally exorcizing the artist), a bewildered child, and a woman wearing a veil, so only her eyes can be seen (was she trying to say something?).

I pointed out to Helen that the people seated in front of Marina always mimicked her position. Although there was no clearly stated rule, it seemed not to have crossed anyone's mind to slouch on the minimalist wooden chair.

This made the art student smile slightly, and I left her to her upcoming experience with the artist and went to speak with Marco.

I was curious to know if he was taking pictures randomly, or instead choosing the moment. He said he usually waited at least ten minutes. Then, he explained, people's faces changed—something was unleashed and revealed.

In the meantime, the line had gotten shorter.

Soon it was my turn.

I walked to the chair.

My heart beating, I sat down.

I did my best to sit in front of the artist with the appropriate seriousness.

But when she lifted up her eyes, Marina didn't seem particularly enthusiastic.

I felt like a forgotten lump of clay on a sculpture stand, half dry, and not very enticing, so that after a little consideration the artist finally decides not to use it.

I felt like another mile in the endless journey of a truck driver.

I thought of Marina's performance as a living illustration of the philosophical concept of how art looks back at us.

Was Marina hypnotizing me ? I became incredibly relaxed and felt a tremendous urge to sleep.

Images of the full MoMA collection were flying by in my head, along with high-lights from the Prado and never-shown pieces from the Louvre reserve.

I watched black-and-white 16mm footage of early '70s performances, when girls in the audience wore printed miniskirts, and men wore wide ties on fitted white shirts, spectacles, and long beards—similar to those of today, but with outstanding genuineness.

I was woken up by a nightmarish vision of Marina's *Dragon Heads*, a series of pieces where she had big snakes all around her face.

How long had I slept? Many of the visitors were in awe.

Walking out, I passed in front of a group of people who seemed offended. In doubt, I apologized for possibly snoring.

Julian

Juergen

Claude

Sophie

Alex

Greg

Mario

A New York Stroll

I saw a man and a dog making their bed in a brand new condo on Flatbush Avenue.

I was painting watercolors of the New Jersey sunset, and saw a solitary man catching a small fish from the pier.

On a yacht moored in Battery Park, a man with a red turban was presiding to an intimate dinner, exposed to the Saturday passersby.

And I walked to 23rd Street and 8th Avenue, to see if the automat where (as told in *Just Kids*) Allen Ginsberg once bought a sandwich for Patti Smith, thinking she was a boy, still exists.

Trisha Brown at Dia:Beacon

A few weeks ago I was invited to the benefit at Dia:Beacon.

The Michael Heizer sculpture *North, East, South, West,* the most powerful and impressive piece one might find in an indoor art space, was open to the art patrons so they could walk around the vertiginous holes. Physical confrontation with the geometric void was in fact so overwhelming that even the most self-assured art experts and trustees would only bend over in the most overcautious manner, fearing loss of glasses, cell phones, or dignity (by having to be winched up from the depths of art by a crane).

When all the guests were finally safely gathered in the John Chamberlain room, Dia director Philippe Vergne announced that, as a surprise and special treat, Trisha Brown will perform a dance piece herself.

She silently came out barefoot, and very slowly began to animate parts of her body upon contact with the other dancers. It started out with very light and delicate touches of fingers and palms. The graceful fragility of hands, wrists, and necks made for a moving contrast with the surrounding heavy metal, the brutally bent and hammered car parts of the Chamberlain sculpture that stood next to the soft flexible bodies of the dancers.

A sartorial note: it was hard to figure out the dress code for this kind of event, when everyone has to get noticed while blending in. For the men, the formal outfits most common were tight, pastel cashmere cardigans, as if dressed for a picnic, while a few individuals met the occasion with bolder statements.

A rival hipster, Kenneth Goldsmith, made it on to several blogs wearing a paisley Thom Browne suit.

The Faux Baldessari
(A True Story)

On my last stay in Paris, I went into a supermarket, and in that most mundane surrounding, my eyes were suddenly attracted by an unusual but somehow familiar silhouette.

A very tall, white-haired and bearded man, wearing a green turtleneck, slightly worn khakis, and carrying a cool tote bag, was walking down the aisle, giving a gentle but slightly amused stare at everything that came his way. A benevolent giant, or a Dutch hippie? Suddenly I was reminded of somebody: John Baldessari, the great conceptual artist! Could it be him?

I had met him seventeen years ago in New York. He had a show then in a gallery in Soho, and he had shaken my hand after he had signed a small poster printed on tracing paper for me.

Although it was a bit surprising to see him in this dull Paris supermarket, it could have been because of the forthcoming Art Basel fair, about to open in Switzerland in a few days. It wasn't illogical that he would have made a quick stop to Paris on his way to say hello to his dealers, or even to discuss a major retrospective at Beaubourg.

Mr. Baldessari…? I hesitated to greet him among the other customers.

In the same way a pale blue or yellow dot added to an insignificant black-and-white photograph becomes a Baldessari, I immediately visualized how the whole supermarket had been turned into a Baldessari by the simple presence of the famous L.A. artist in its insignificant aisle.

I wondered if anyone else had recognized him. While debating on whether keeping a discreet distance to respect his incognito, or approaching him to confess my admiration, I saw him strolling away with one or two whisky bottles in his tote bag, followed by a pigeon, in the direction of the Luxembourg garden.

I was delighted the whole day by this poetic vision, although already saddened by the prospect of never seeing him again, and having wasted the chance of a great encounter.

Two days after, on a sultry evening, I saw the man again. He was swaying on the wide boulevard sidewalk, his pants half unbuttoned and covered with dirt, dragging his tote bag, with a somewhat demented and defiant look on his face.

As if to add insult to my delusion, Art Basel was approaching its end, and the bum who could then onward commonly be seen in various states of decay became a fixture in the area.

Street Watch

This spring, herds of dudes are hitting the streets in tight shorts. I carefully studied the look, and it seems the more untanned the legs, the tighter and darker the short pants.

When I say "untanned," I mean the legs should look as if they have been forgotten in the CBGB basement for twenty five years, and a sales assistant at John Varvatos just excavated them from under piles of shoe boxes. It's a smart urban look, good enough to attend civilized events and great for cycling at night if you've got no rear light.

Cut Pieces

On Fashion's Night Out this year, the art galleries of Chelsea were as mobbed as the shopping sidewalks of Soho.

At D'Amelio Terras, the visitors had to be queued so as not to all at once storm the Polly Apfelbaum installation. In a piece titled *Off Colour* the artist had cut and arranged sequined stretch fabric in colors inspired from a stack of erotic slides bought in a London flea market.

Although most viewers were carefully navigating through the piece's negative space, some pieces of fabrics, simply laid on the gallery floor, were disturbed out of place by the more distracted visitors—or those equipped with oversized shoes— leading the artist to readjust the pieces in an unpremeditated performance.

I then had to elbow my way down to the MoMA store in Soho, where Adi, Gabi, and Angela from threeASFOUR were paying tribute to Yoko Ono's 1964 *Cut Piece* by cutting into their own design worn by a model. Adi was wearing a dress printed with drawings by Yoko, from the previous collection.

A wide range of scissors were available to the participating viewers, and when my turn came, I was torn between the wish to not damage my friends' design with the desire to reveal more of the stunning beauty.

A Journey to Tokyo

Early this autumn I was invited to attend Tokyo Graphic Passport, a creative and visual arts conference organized by *+81* magazine, a Japanese graphic design journal, with speakers coming from various parts of the world.

I love Tokyo. From the very first time (back in the early '90s, when I came as the lead tambourine player for Uneven Dusk to perform gigs at a small club located in the basement of an anonymous white-tile building in the outskirts of Tokyo), I was taken by the poetic particularities of that city, and have taken every chance I can to come back.

I love the crazy sound of cicadas in the summer, the temples and their gardens, the tiny bars, and the blinking red lights atop the office towers at night. I can stroll endlessly in the quiet backstreets behind the busiest arteries, and wish I could live in one of these little wood houses. Even the spectacular flagship stores of the global luxury brands seem like surrealistic mysteries, and yet appear more gentle there than anywhere else.

Fantasista Utamaro performing at Arts Chiyoda

"Live Painting," as it's called, is a common and much appreciated form of performance art for painters and their public, just like readings are for American writers—although anybody who has ever painted could sense that it's less than likely that a painting executed in public would be any good. Even Picasso was not so astonishing in the film *Le mystère Picasso*. But Fantasista managed to get his act together in front his home crew.

John Warwicker from Tomato had flown from Australia to paint a large mural.

If the mural was John's, the stained plastic protections on the floor were reminiscent of Hans Namuth's photos of Pollock. Most amazingly, John's painting looked good at all the different stages throughout the three days it took to finish.

These young chaps had looks that deserve a Sartorialist award

While Roland Barthes's *Empire of Signs* is my beloved travel companion in Japan and a nourishing read, it's sometimes more nutritious to dine on sumo food.

What I like to do most in Tokyo is to get away from the main shopping areas and wander into the less-known neighborhoods, which in my mind must look more like what Tokyo used to be. I wish I had first traveled there not just ten years before they shot *Lost in Translation* and made Tokyo a cliché, but back in the '60s or '70s, when photographers were taking distorted black-and-white nudes, Hondas were small and painted mustard yellow or pea green, and the "modern" women wore strict European dresses and listened to classical music in dark, hi-fi parlours in the afternoon.

I soon found myself walking in Jinbocho, which is the secondhand bookstores district. It's a bit like the Strand in New York, if the Strand was laid flat on its back and split in hundreds of small shops, with piles and piles of books on the sidewalk. This is when my eyes caught the window of an old-fashioned eyewear shop. On display were faded photographs of John Lennon and round-shaped spectacles, all displayed on emerald-green and flesh-pink satin.

The shop was a happy clutter inside and seemed untouched since the late '70s, with more John Lennon posters and more vintage Lennon spectacles. There were collections of old optometric paraphernalia, and an old, abandoned VCR, which I suppose once played Lennon's tapes.

A lady came down the wooden stairs, inquiring in Japanese.

Soon it became obvious that we couldn't communicate, besides nodding and smiling to each other.

"So you must like John Lennon very much," I articulated in a last attempt with my French accent, actually hoping she would not understand such a tired line.

She took a cell phone, dialed a number, and after briefly speaking into it, passed it on to me.

A man's voice spoke a few English words, with a noisy crowd in the background, which made him even more difficult to understand.

"I wanted to tell the lady that it's a lovely shop," I shouted.

"What?"

"I would like to know the name and address so I could write it down in my blog!"

I was thinking of you, dear readers, at this particular moment (although perhaps hundreds of bloggers and guides might already have listed this information), but finally had to admit to myself that the conversation was going nowhere, with the crowd in the background of the cell phone getting louder. Maybe he was off betting somewhere, or in a busy railway station.

I asked the lady for a card, mimicking the object. She gave me a piece of imitation chamois leather, inscribed with something in Japanese and, at last, a phone number: 03-3291-0279.

I bowed and retreated to the door. On my way out, I stopped in front of a framed picture of a white dog.

"Your dog…? Lovely dog!"

But didn't insist, thinking that the fact the dog's picture was framed meant he might not be there anymore.

I bowed once more, and was out.

In a time when everybody is willing to sell his soul in a minute in fear of being out of date, such faith and fidelity should be praised. I think it's true gentleness.

And only if I have had access to this shop when I was a young kid, when I was craving Lennon glasses.

Acting Jobs

As I have mentioned before, once in a while I model for French *GQ*. This commercial commitment allows me to write difficult poetry and compose experimental music for tambourine in my free time without having to take into account what the public may want.

Modeling is much tougher than it appears. Especially when—in my case, for instance—it's more of a acting job. To be clear: modeling is for sissies and the Actor's Studio is for tough guys. Needless to say, you always throw in a sensitive note now and then to add heartbreaking depth to the most physical performances.

I've made this selection of seven shots that give, I think, a good idea of the breadth and richness of my interpretations.

No. 1

No matter how laid-back you are, you can't pretend to be an actor (or even model) unless you're a true athlete. See how the other dude in this shot, a three-time winner of the Jokari World Championship, is paralyzed by my technique.

Exhibiting true athleticism

Demonstrating indifference to hostility

No. 2

Here I'm demonstrating my disregard to pander as a DJ by playing an entire Joanna Newsom track amid a hostile crowd. Note that the RPM was slowed by 40 percent for total chill-out effect.

Extending friendship to all (even extras)

No. 3

Part of the job is that you have to work with a wide variety of folks. I don't remember exactly what was the point of this shot. It was right after lunch break. Maybe I went back in the wrong studio.

Drawing on my Method training

No. 4

A tricky one: how to attract the attention of a French waiter?

For this, I drew on my own experience of long hours spent in cafés, which was not really to my benefit: how do you quantify such an expertise, gained at the expense of your own pocket money? You always end up being paid less than what you deserved!

Of course, the guy in a white jacket is not a real waiter, as he would have never turned his head in my direction.

Sacrificing for authenticity

No. 5

Another odd one: I was directed to demonstrate how to drink from a shoe, with impeccable style and manners. If one has to pour champagne in a shoe, it seemed obvious to me that my waterproof old Red Wings were the most appropriate container.

No. 6

The job has its highs and lows of dignity. Here I was asked to show how to light up a match before leaving the bathroom as a courtesy to the next user. I had never heard of this, but according to French *GQ*, it's customary to do so. (Beware of doing it in a plane though.) The explosion that ensued shook the whole building and broke the rear window of the stylist's Fiat 500 parked round the corner.

No. 7

When to use or not use a cell phone is a heady question. When I asked a young assistant her opinion, she explained that what's impolite is to not multitask while being with someone: it gives your companion the awkward sense of being with somebody of less importance.

The shoot took hours. To have the girls right together all at once was the most difficult. Paul, the art director, had to stand on a chair and yell in a microphone, waving a red flag to get their attention.

And in the overheated studio, the girls had to get their makeup redone every fifteen minutes, even though the image was to be retouched by the famous Pascal Dangin. Just for my beard, Pascal had to work five hours to get rid of bread crumbs left by a bruschetta from the delicious catering.

Maintaining absolute concentration in the face of distraction

Vincent

Terry

a.a.

Gildas and Masaya

André

Kanye

Olivier

In Conversation With:
The Central Park Coyote

I was crossing Central Park a few nights ago. There was a school party at the ice-skating rink, and you could hear the booming music in the distance.

It was on a lonely path just by the pond that I saw the coyote, standing very still, and looking straight at me. I had just read about the coyote in the park in *New York* magazine, but thought it was an hoax aimed at making their readers believe in urban magic while they're in line at Whole Foods.

"Hi," said the coyote.

"Man, I thought you were an hoax ! But now I can see you're for real, and you even speak!"

"Dude, do you like Indian music?" he asked. To which I had no answer.

"I mean, do you believe in reincarnation and all that shit?"

I always thought reincarnation was an hoax as well, but I didn't tell the coyote, so as not to hurt his feelings.

"The last time I was born," he went on, "was in the middle of Walter de Maria's *Lightning Field*. Until I was a grown up I thought it was genuine Nature, and then somebody told me it was Art. From that moment on, the landscape lost all its mysteries. I thought about moving to L.A., but finally decided to walk all the way back to New York. I first went to the Bowery, where I was a cool cat in the '50s, renting a studio next to de Kooning, and advising Robert Frank on *Pull My Daisy*. I was on and off through the '60s, and became a regular at CBGB where I replaced the Ramones drummer for a set once, when he was too drunk to play. But in 2009, the Bowery was no more a place for me. And I took the 6 train—which I had tagged in the early '80s—up to Central Park. Here I can hide in the bushes and get Smart water from the pond. I also study Uptown people, since I was more familiar with the Downtown crowd. Of course, there are loads of tourists, but the whole town became very touristy anyway. Well, New York is no more what it used to be. It's all fake and loud, a big shopping mall mainly populated by self-obsessed dogs. Only the architecture remains."

Seeing him becoming bitter, I asked him if the coyote in Joseph Beuys's piece *I Like America and America Likes Me* was a relative.

"No, but I knew him," he replied. "He was such an asshole." (Meaning the coyote, not the famous artist.) "He certainly was not qualified for the job, totally illiterate with art, and besides a real wimp. But he had a strong drive for celebrity, and schemed to be cast for the role. In fact, another coyote, a true wild one, had been selected, but he went loose a few days before the performance started, and had to be replaced by this phony at the last minute. I'm glad he got hit by the cane a few times. See, being locked in a cage with Beuys was not like being in an hotel room with Jeff Koons."

"Have you seen the Abramovic show at MoMA ? It's really impressive."

"Not yet, I hope they'll let me in. I was refused at the Whitney Biennial."

I wondered if he ever gets bored with monotonous days in the park.

"I have lots of activities. Escaping from the cops. Stealing sandwiches from Uptown kids while their crews of nannies gossip together. Aboriginal art with dirt and stones. African wood carvings. And on Wednesday nights, I perform Native American dances, right by this oak. Free admission, no photos."

Royal Wedding

I was in London the other day, just leaving Mr Bongo, where I had scored some great vinyls, when I was caught in a huge gathering.

The crowd seemed to have been staking out positions on the sidewalk for at least a day or two, with camping chairs and sleeping bags. I stopped by a group holding British flags and asked them what was going on. Troops in period costume and horse carriages passed by at that moment, and I wondered whether they were shooting some Hollywood film, or maybe even a fashion event, as I heard people saying that Sarah Burton at Alexander McQueen had designed the royal wedding dress.

All of a sudden, there was a deep silence, followed by a giant roar from the crowd as the Queen's carriage passed by. I couldn't help but shed a tear of emotion when I saw her waving a hand in our direction.

Uninvited, I tried to make myself discreet

To be of some use, I joined the choir

I was just following some fellows who seemed to know where they were going

Sensing my embarrassment, the Queen mercifully asked me what kind of records I had bought at Mr Bongo

The Selby is in the
Unknown Hipster's Place

When The Selby called to ask whether he could photograph my place, it was a nice surprise, of course, but I thought I should warn him.

"You know, it's kind of small ..."

"Don't tell me it's smaller than Rockaway Taco! Don't be shy, I'm sure it's wonderful!"

But then I completely forgot all about it, and suddenly, on a stormy afternoon, it was Todd knocking on my door.

The bed was unmade since I was taking a little nap, and the kitchen was cluttered with the remains of yesterday's spaghetti Bolognese (one day I'll share my recipe, taught to me by an Italian grandmother). But what the hell, I thought, Todd is cool, he has done a lot of artists and bohemians. I didn't think he was expecting my pad to be as slick as Pharrell Williams's home.

Welcome to the secluded home of a poet!

But when he walked in, I could see disappointment and a little bit of anxiety on his face.

"What's that funny smell . . ." he said.

True, I just had a new goatskin shipped from Morocco for my tambourine, and since it's 100 percent organic, there's a bit of an odor when the weather is hot and humid. But no big deal; one quickly gets used to it.

I used to grow pot on the fire escape, but the plants died while I was out attending Fashion Week last year. All I could offer him was a nice cup of Nescafé, straight out of the hot-water tap.

Todd is a warm and sweet character with a great sense of humor, and he knows immediately how to make you feel at ease in your own place. I was amazed, though, by his way of working. I was imagining him firing detail shots with the EOS. On the contrary, he was carefully looking at my stacks of cassettes tapes and my secondhand *Beat Reader* from the Strand.

I suggested that I play the guitar on my bed, thinking it would make a great wide-angle panoramic shot for the opening.

"Thanks," said Todd, "but let me just do a quick close-up, and I'll do a little water-color from home." And he's off, running down the stairs, forgetting to hand me his questionnaire.

Questionnaires, even from friends, are always a pain for me. I admire the spontaneity of some people when it comes to this. I studied the answers of my pals, Glenn, Andy, Xavier, and Pierre. How did they manage to do it? It took me four weeks to fill it out. Hope it's okay.

An Ironing Class
at Colette

It's one thing to be possessed by clothes, it's another to own them.

This is why Colette, during this last July's Men's Shows in Paris, held an ironing class exclusively for men in its basement Water Bar.

It is no irony to think that this would prevent some of the fashion obsessed among us from running their shirts to the nearest cleaner (if not their mums), and likely to return a Junya Watanabe in the state of a stretch of toilet paper.

A dozen ironing tables had been installed like a classroom, all equipped with Rowenta steam power stations which were as intimidating as a Hummer for those who have never driven before.

Jocelyne, a professor at the École de Gouvernantes et Majordomes, started by teaching us the meaning of washing instructions icons. For some, it was already too late—their shirt had probably shrunk three sizes. A student raised his arm in alarm that a symbol inside his shirt was not mentioned in Jocelyn's exhaustive list.

"Is it Japanese?" she asked, raising her eyebrows. The dude confirmed: it was a Tsumori Chisato. "Well, if it's Japanese ..." and she shrugged with a smile.

A customer puzzled by the scene

Jocelyne proudly wearing her medal of Meilleure Ouvrière de France

Several unexperienced scenesters, in fear of being unsubscribed from the newsletter by bringing the wrong shirt, had brought their best attire—all fresh from the washing machine, crumbled like a handkerchief long forgotten in a back pocket.

Writer and blogger Borey meticulously working his shirt

For my part, I had brought one of my signature worn-out flea-market plaid shirts. Some of the dudes glanced over at it with envy, thinking it was an advance sample from Maison Kitsuné's "Brokeback Mountain" collection.

In fact, I had just got it back from the cleaner, and had to pull it into a ball and sit on it during my Métro ride over, so it would be wrinkled enough to be ironed.

Jocelyne looked over my shoulder while I was passing over a part of the collar that had stayed flat from the cleaner, and congratulated me.

When we finally came to the folding lesson—how keeping our folds symmetrical so that one shoulder is not twice as wide as the other—there was very little time left for the pants.

This saved me from the ridiculous dilemma of having to iron the torn jeans I had brought in a plastic bag, or confess to Jocelyn that I never wear any other sort of pants.

A participant discovers the complexity of ironing.

Terry

Jarance and Scott

Waris, Olivier, and André

A Few Things I Saw on the 9/11 Anniversary

In Battery Park, a man shadowboxing as the fireboat slowly passed by with its hoses turned on.

A man looking like Jeff Bridges in a rescue team movie, except this was the real thing.

Paul Simon sings "The Sound of Silence."
A police officer wipes his eyes at the end of the song.

A thundering biker stops for photos.

An Installation by
Andy Spade

A couple of weeks ago Andy did a one-day installation at the Half Gallery.

In a work entitled *Casa Grande AZ 1972–1975*, thirty cacti of various species were arrayed on the floor, while black ballons floated above, up against the ceiling.

As the gallery text stated: "Andy Spade's first solo show offers a glimpse into his youth growing up in a small Arizona town. In a household with a new stepfather, he and his brothers felt the tension between his fits of rage and depression and his mother's blind, yet always sunny disposition. This installation represents the sublimation of childhood disenfranchisement."

The deflating balloons would explode when they floated low enough to touch the cacti, and their number gradually diminished.

This slow but inevitable process went on all night behind the gallery's closed door.

Carine in a gold vintage dress

Carine's Karaoke

Out of boredom on a recent Saturday afternoon, I was trying out some pants at Supreme when my friend Victoire called to ask if I wouldn't mind accompanying her to the party being given by Barneys for Carine Roitfeld.

A few minutes later, as I was walking with renewed energy on Lafayette Street, she called again: "They want to know what our favorite songs are—it's karaoke!"

Had I gone to Tokyo at least fifteen times and always successfully avoided karaoke parties, to finally get trapped into one in New York? Is there a more depressing scene than drunks trying to read the lyrics on a TV screen to blaring '80s hits?

But, of course, as masterminded by Carine, it was going to be something else, and with high anticipation we made our approach to Westway, the former strip club, where the party was happening.

Limousines were jammed on Clarkson Street, and squads of "it" girls and models on high heels were carefully navigating the cobblestones, exposing their million-dollar legs to the outdoor spotlights.

I was in fear that somebody would push me on the stage, just for fun. What would I sing? The only song I know is Syd Barrett's "Effervescing Elephant."

It turned out to be the most professional karaoke event one could witness. The fashion people all hit the stage—which look rather like a catwalk—with stunning confidence. Not only did they never sing out of tune, but they could also dance across the stage back and forth doing all the things performers do, like pointing at the crowd (and probably pole dancing as well).

The flashes on iPhones burnt out during Anna dello Russo's number

The Italians were especially good. Even the seasoned fashion assistants must have changed their minds when they realized their most-feared celebrities were showing genuine warmth, good humor, and sincere emotions. Everybody sensed a historical moment when Valentino's rendition of "My Way" almost one-upped Sinatra's Vegas version.

Valentino singing "My Way"

As we left the party and walked along the West Side Highway with imagined scenes of endless rehearsals in burgundy bathrobes late at night in the privacy of the hotel's palace suite, a small anonymous car overloaded with men suddenly pulled along the sidewalk. All the doors opened at once and the passengers burst out like undercover policemen about to seize somebody.

A young lad in a torn T-shirt ran out of the car to take refuge against a wall, where he theatrically faced his pursuers. Among the gang's sinister faces, we were relieved to recognize Terry Richardson's, thanks to his plaid shirt and signature moustache. This time he didn't have his thumbs up but was aiming his Powershot at the young actor.

Terry immediately started to fire flashes at his subject, who obligingly gave varied poses.

It seemed the complete New York fashion scene had decided to unfold in just one night.

Occupy Wall Street

Last Sunday evening I went down to Liberty Park to see the Wall Street protesters. It had snowed the day before, and I wondered whether they were still there.

The protesters were huddling in an assembly, and were using their now-iconic "human microphone" to speak, with the crowd repeating the speaker's short phrases.

And I think

I THINK

This is

THIS IS

A useful invention

A USEFUL INVENTION

Which gives any sentence

WHICH GIVES ANY SENTENCE

The tone

THE TONE

And shape

AND SHAPE

Of an art form

AN ART FORM

Which

WHICH

Turns

TURNS

The ordinary

THE ORDINARY

Into the poetic

INTO THE POETIC

And gives gravity

GIVES GRAVITY

And exceptional weight

AND EXCEPTIONAL WEIGHT

To unnoticed words

UNNOTICED WORDS

And accidental

AND ACCIDENTAL

comical absurdity

COMICAL ABSURDITY

To excessive solemnity.

EXCESSIVE SOLEMNITY.

I thought the Dadaist poets or the early Situationists, in particular the Lettrists, would have liked it.

Serious kids with long hair and angelic faces listened raptly to bums and fools.

Where art thou, Isidore Isou?

Front Row

It was the last flight at JFK, and the boarding of the giant A380 seemed to never end, when recognizing Grace Coddington seated by herself in the first-class front row reminded me that Paris Fashion Week was about to start.

For all who saw the *The September Issue* and fell under her charm, Grace seems to possess the disillusionment of a true philosopher while being more of an artist than most photographers—more of an artist, in fact, than most artists who'd rather have their new summer house featured in *Vogue* than their last show reviewed in *Art Forum* (although, of course, both are necessary).

I was lost in my reflections about Grace when I was suddenly brought back to reality by a "Can I see your invitation?" I was then urged along with the herd to the standing row by a flight attendant who had the fierce insensitivity of a PR assistant.

Listening to Glenn

At the opening of *Dressed for Art* at fi:af, Glenn O'Brien arrived with a large bag, from which he pulled out a bullhorn to read some of his poems.

Plain

Give me a plain.

Make it a medium plain.

No, I don't want anything in it.

You don't have any medium?

Only large, extra large,

But don't fill it up all the way.

Glenn is the only poet who understands the relationship between fashion and the commercial world. Once I heard him read "Beatnik Executives," one of my favorite poems, in the Barneys store:

I saw the best minds of my generation

Depressed by lawsuits, dieting, sober, all dressed up,

. . .

Angel-headed hipsters renegotiating the social contract,

Trying to renegotiate the lease on life

And cool this microwaved world.*

Besides having been photographed in his pants by Andy Warhol for the cover of *Sticky Fingers,* he is the only poet who has written on the subject of "How to Be a Man," a philosopher's take on sartorial subjects that extends to questions like "the correct insult" and "what to do after death and how to deal with eternity."

Most poets try to bring you down to make a living, but Glenn provides workable solutions for life:

When I get confused or dismayed or bored I always think:

but what if this was an art movie.*

*Excerpts from Soapbox: Essays, Diatribes, Homilies and Screeds 1980–1997, *Imschoot Uitgevers, 1998*

"The Happening"

THE BIRTH OF THE UNKNOWN HIPSTER

In the spring of 2009, I had an exhibition at Partners & Spade for the launch of my book *The Cultivated Life*. I had done a series of color-pencil drawings called *The Purple Celebrities*, which were portraits of the most featured characters in the *Purple Diary*, the blog of *Purple Magazine*'s Olivier Zahm: Terry, Dash, Waris, Vincent Gallo, Mario, Juergen, and of course the *Diary*'s superstar himself, Olivier.

When the gallery assistant checked the names for the price list, she asked me about the drawing of a bearded man with long hair, plaid shirt, jeans, white jacket, and plain heavy-duty tote bag that she didn't recognize. Who is it? she asked.

This was nobody in particular, or rather, a ubiquitous man that I was often coming across on the sidewalks of the Bowery, and who seemed a reincarnation of the hippies I had admired so much when I was a child.

"It's a hipster," I said.
"Which hipster?"
"Unknown."
"Unknown Hipster," she asked? "Is this the title?"
"Yes, Unknown Hipster."
The Unknown Hipster was born.

JPhD

Index

_____

ACKNOWLEDGMENTS

My first thanks are to Dung Ngo, who from the start and all along the way edited and encouraged the Unknown Hipster, and to Martine Trélaün, who researched and organized the Unknown Hipster's files and designed this book.

To Nicholas Mir Chaikin, from Spill, who set up the blog.
To Sarah from Colette, who was among the first friends of the Unknown.
To Garance Doré, who posted about it from an Australian Fashion Week, and within a flight from Paris to New York the views jumped from 213 to 18,500.
To Andy Spade, who exhibited the first known portrait of the Unknown.
I would like to extend my thanks to Paul Chemetoff and
Anne Boulay at *GQ* in France.
And to Gilda Bojardi and Diana Sung at *GCasa* in Italy.

The Unknown Hipster expresses his gratitude to all the interesting people featured in these diaries, including Bill Cunningham, Damien Hirst, a Baldessari look-alike, Marina Abramovic, The Selby, Grace Coddington, anonymous models seen on the sidewalk, and a lonesome Central Park coyote.

All drawings were first published in the Unknown Hipster blog except for the drawings from "My Life as a Model" and "Acting Jobs," which were previously published in *GQ* France. The drawing from "John Pawson's Monastery" was previously published in *GCasa* Italy.

Jean-Philippe Delhomme